W9-BSP-558

WREN

Books by Marie Killilea

KAREN

WREN

Wren

by MARIE KILLILEA

ILLUSTRATED BY BOB RIGER

DODD, MEAD & COMPANY
NEW YORK

Library of Congress Catalog Card Number: 54-9509

Printed in the United States of America

TO MY BLESSED MOTHER

CONTENTS

The characters in this book are all
real and the situations
all true

WREN

CHAPTER ONE

THE SPECIAL PRESENT

IN a town by the sea there was a real little girl and her name was really Marie. She lived with her mother and father in a sweet brown house. The house had a steep roof, a big stone chimney and flowers around it.

Marie was a very happy and pretty little girl. (Happiness makes people pretty, you know.) Her father called her his "Laughing Princess" and like many princesses she had golden curls—not long, but tight to her head like a shiny cap.

One warm summer day she was happier and prettier than usual. It was her BIRTHDAY!

She had waited a long time for this birthday and for a very *special* present her mother and father had promised. They told her this present would make her happier than anything in the whole wide world. She had thought and thought but couldn't guess what it was.

Mummy and Daddy always hid her birthday presents because she had such fun hunting for them.

This day she hunted under her bed and found a pair of ice skates for her doll—under a chair she found a book about a white rabbit called *Marshmallow*—behind the sofa cushion she found a new dress and some hair ribbons to match—behind the front door she found a ball and in the piano bench she found a magnifying glass.

Each time she discovered a present she would say, "*This* is the *special* one," and her mother and father would laugh and tell her:

"No, not that one. It is far more exciting than that."

When Marie thought she had found all the presents, she saw a big box under her father's chair. She ran over, pulled it out and tore off the lid. It was a beautiful French doll with high heel shoes.

"This is it!" She fairly screamed—she was so excited. Her mother and father laughed even more than before and told her—"No."

She looked at them in wonder, thinking that nothing could be better than this.

Mummy whispered in her ear, "The special present hasn't come yet. We will tell you the very moment it does."

"It can't be better than my doll." Marie was sure of that.

"You'll see," Daddy teased and gave Mummy a kiss. This reminded Marie of something and she jumped up and ran to them and kissed and squeezed them both. "Thank you! Thank you!" And she kissed them again.

Marie decided to call her new doll Denise and her mother and father agreed that this was a perfect name for a little French lady.

The next morning Marie woke just when the birds were talking about their breakfasts. She stood her doll up on the window sill so she could see them, too. "Look," Marie told her doll, "look how funny that

fat robin walks." After watching the birds for a while, she asked, "What do you think my special present will be?" But Denise didn't tell.

Just then Marie's father ran into the room. He grabbed her and hugged her. "Your present's here. It's here!" he shouted and danced around the room with Marie in his arms.

"Where is it? What it is? I want to see it quick. Put me down, Daddy, and tell me quick—please." Daddy dumped Marie on the bed and she bounced.

"It's a real live baby—"

"*Oh-o-o-o,* Daddy! Can I see it? Can I see it?"

"Not right now, Princess. We have to wait a couple of days."

"Is it a boy baby like Kathy's or a girl like Denise?"

"It's a girl baby—"

"Where is she?"

"She and Mummy are in the hospital where they do special things for new babies."

"What's her name?"

"Karen—Karen Killilea."

"That's pretty. Will she be home today?"

"Not for a few days, Princess," answered her father. "She's going to be your baby, you know. You can take care of her."

"Like I take care of my dolls?" She hugged Denise.

"Yes." Her father put his arm around her. "Now let's say 'thank-you' to God for this wonderful present."

So they knelt down together and folded their hands and closed their eyes and thought about how good God was and together they said:

"Thank you God for rain and sun,
For knowing You, Most Loving One,
For friends and home and country free,
For all the blessings given me—especially our new baby girl."

CHAPTER TWO

WAITING

MARIE took very good care of Denise. She washed and pressed the ribbons for her dress and hair. She twisted her curls around her finger and brushed them until they shone. She listened to records with her doll in her arms (she liked the *Nutcracker Suite* best) and danced with her and when she went to bed, she sat Denise on a chair beside her like a proper little lady.

Marie thought about Karen a lot. She thought about her when she went to bed. She thought about her when she was skipping rope or just lying in the grass. She thought what fun it was going to be to have a toy that she didn't have to wind or pull to make it move. She thought about Kathy's baby brother, John, and how tiny his hands were. She thought about the wonderful soft noises babies made. That was something dolls didn't do.

Every night when her father came home, Marie would run to meet him and ask, "When are Mummy and Karen coming home, Daddy?"

Then, one lovely evening, her father came dashing up the street like a boy and threw open the door. "Princess, tomorrow Mummy is coming home!"

Marie jumped up and down. "I can't wait—I can't wait to see Karen."

Her father made a face, almost as though she had said something wrong. She felt unhappy, so she went over and took his hand. He smiled down at her. "Karen is still very little, Sweetheart. She's only as big as Denise. In the hospital they know how to do things to make babies grow big and strong, so we're going to leave Karen there for a little while longer."

Marie was so happy to have her mother home that she forgot about Karen for two whole days. It was wonderful to have Mummy to play with and to lie beside her until she fell asleep.

One cold afternoon, Marie and Kathy were putting some raisins and fat in a little wooden box for the birds to eat. "I want to see Karen," stated Kathy.

"You can't," said Marie.

"Why not? I let you play with John."

"She's too little, that's why she has to stay in the hospital."

"Will she ever get big?"

"Yes."

"When?"

"I—I don't know."

Just then Marie's mother called, "Come for dinner, Princess."

Marie kicked at the snow as she went up the hill from Kathy's house. She was thinking dinner wasn't so much fun any more. There wasn't time for jokes and games while they did the dishes, because

Mummy and Daddy had to hurry to the hospital so they could see Karen. Then Marie smiled. Anyway, she stayed up later and they told her about her baby when they came home. Then she stopped smiling. She was waiting an awfully long time for her special present. Years and years.

While she was eating her dinner that evening Marie asked her mummy, 'What do you DO at the hospital?"

"We look and look and look," she answered, "and then, because I have such a poor voice, I whistle to her. I whistle all the nursery rhymes. She just loves it. She smiles and makes noises and yesterday she pursed her lips almost as if she were trying to whistle, too."

"I'm going to ask Santa Claus to bring her home for Christmas, so she can play with my presents, too."

"She won't be big enough by Christmas," her mother told Marie, "but we'll take presents to her—lots of them."

"Won't she ever be home?"

Her father answered her. "Of course she will. When she's big and strong enough."

John, Kathy's baby brother, was real big and certainly strong and Marie couldn't understand why it took so long for Karen to get big and strong.

She and her mother wrote Santa Claus a letter and asked him for a sled and paints and books and a small tennis racquet for Marie and a picture book and a rattle with a bell inside and a wooly lamb for Karen.

The days went very slowly before Christmas. Marie sometimes thought that Christmas would never come at all. . . . But it did come (as Christmas always does) and Santa had decorated the tree with twinkling lights and strands of silver and oodles and oodles of shiny ornaments. He had piled her gifts around the tree and—believe it or not—she found every single thing she had asked for and Santa had not forgotten anything she had wanted for Karen.

The sled was long and shiny and slipped ever so fast over the snow. Marie took Denise sleigh riding once and it was great fun.

After a while there wasn't any more snow. The air began to feel warm, and grass that had been hiding all winter began to turn green. One day Marie's mother said, "It will soon be Easter, Sweetheart."

And her father said, "We're going to ask Dr. John if we can bring Karen home soon now."

"Hurray!" Marie did a little dance. Dr. John was her dear, good friend. When she was sick he always made her well in a hurry. He would make Karen big and strong quick.

Marie and her family always went to church together on Sunday. One Sunday, right after they arrived home, Dr. John came to the house. Marie ran up and took his hand and they walked together over to Mummy and Daddy.

Dr. John was smiling at everybody as he said, "Karen is big and strong enough to come home. She'll be ready to leave the hospital tomorrow morning."

The hill behind Marie's house sloped down to a short little street that had only ten houses on it. It was called Vale Place and it was here that most of Marie's friends lived. Now that she had this good news, she rushed skidding and sliding down the hill. From house to house she ran, shouting, "Karen's coming home! Tomorrow—tomorrow—tomorrow!"

The children tumbled out of their houses and chased each other up the hill to Marie's. There were big girls and little girls, big boys and little boys—and their dogs, big ones and little ones. They thought this was some new and very exciting game so they barked and the children yelled.

The noise was wonderful!

Marie woke very early the next morning. She ran into her mother's and father's room and jumped on the bed. "It's time to go for Karen. She won't like to wait. I don't." The words spilled out. "Her crib looks so pretty. Did you remember to buy milk, Mummy? Can I really feed her and dress her?"

"She's your baby," her mother assured her.

Mrs. Ruddy came to stay with Marie while her mother and father went to get Karen. Marie could not stay still. She went from room to room. She looked at the crib. She looked at the bottles. She took the tops off jars and peered inside. She patted the pile of diapers. Each time she heard a car coming up the street she ran to the door. She thought they would never come.

Marie was fluffing up Denise's dress so she would look nice for Karen, when she heard her daddy call from the door, "Princess—we're home."

She ran into the living room and there was Mummy with a white bundle in her arms. "Sit down, darling, and I'll give her to you." Marie sat down in the rocking chair. Mummy put the bundle in her arms and Marie held them tight around the baby—but not too tight. Karen was asleep. Marie sat still and looked and looked and looked. What a very special present! Karen was even prettier than she had imagined her. Tinier, too. Her hair was gold like Marie's, her mouth was almost round and she had one little hand pushed up against her cheek. Marie looked at the dainty fingers and the nails. They looked like those little tiny shells she gathered on the shore. Karen moved her head.

"You're home, Karen." Marie spoke softly. Karen opened her eyes. They were greenish brown, the color of a country stream. They were large and were staring hard at Marie. Then Karen smiled at her sister.

Marie bent over and kissed her.

Right then and there, eight-month-old Karen did something that is hard to believe, something that girls and boys five and six and even seven years old can't do. This little baby looked at Marie and WHISTLED!

CHAPTER THREE

THE PROMISE

MARIE and Denise and Karen slept in the same room. Marie slept in a medium sized bed that was green and yellow. Denise slept sitting up in the little maple rocker and Karen slept in a little yellow crib.

In the morning Karen would wake them by making sweet cooing noises. Marie would jump out of bed and run across to the crib. Karen always gurgled when she saw her. "She's telling me she loves me," Marie would say proudly to Denise.

Sometimes Marie would forget about Denise for a whole day, it was such fun taking care of Karen. She held her baby sister and gave her the bottle. She was careful to keep the nipple full of milk so Karen would not suck in any air. That would give her a tummy ache. She changed diapers and helped Mummy with Karen's bath. Marie would test the temperature of the water by putting her elbow in it. If it did feel cool or burny hot, then it was just right. Marie would splash water over Karen, who would make funny faces, and then Marie and her mother would have to laugh and, of course, Karen laughed, too. They all decided that Karen was the laughingest baby they had ever seen.

Pretty soon it was Mummy's birthday. Daddy gave her a shiny pin and Marie gave her a wooden penholder she had made. She had painted it very nicely and Mummy was delighted with it. She kissed Marie and said, "Thank you, Princess." But Marie thought her mother did not seem to be as happy as people should on their birthdays. She looked questioningly at Daddy. He didn't seem happy either.

Marie walked slowly down the hill to Kathy's house. Kathy's mummy, Mrs. Ruddy, was just giving John his bath. He was about the same age as Karen but ever so much bigger and stronger. Marie watched him in his tub. He was having a fine time. He kicked his feet and slapped the water with his hands. He grabbed the soap and wash cloth and threw them *out* of the tub and then he pulled the towel off the rack and *into* the tub. There were big puddles on the floor. Mrs. Ruddy scolded John but Marie could tell she didn't really mind. John just sat and looked at his mother and pursed up his lips and went "*br-r-s-s.*" A most impolite sound it was!

"Can he whistle?" Marie asked Mrs. Ruddy.

"Goodness, no, not at this age," Mrs. Ruddy answered.

"Karen can," Marie said proudly.

"I can't believe it," said Mrs. Ruddy and looked as if she didn't.

The next day, when Marie and her mother were giving Karen her bath, Marie said, 'You're not singing today, Mummy, and you didn't even whistle yesterday."

"Didn't I, dear?" Mummy asked, and looked sad. Marie felt sad, too. She didn't want her mother to be unhappy. Something was very wrong.

Karen was lying on her mother's arm and Marie was washing her feet. Marie stopped washing and stood looking at the two little feet—then she looked at Karen's hands. They were very still. They hardly moved at all. She thought, "Karen never sits up like John."

"Mummy, why doesn't Karen kick and splash?" she asked. "Why doesn't she grab things and why doesn't she sit up? I want her to."

"So do I," her mother replied softly and her voice sounded almost as though she were going to cry.

"Why won't she?" Marie asked again.

Her mother turned her face away. "But why?" Marie repeated.

"As soon as we get her to bed, I'll tell you," Mummy said in the same strange, tight voice.

Something *was* wrong. Marie knew it. She had a bad feeling in her stomach, like when she was very hungry and had to wait a long time for her dinner. She sat on the lawn and ate a piece of sour grass. It didn't taste tangy and sharp the way it usually did. She remembered that Daddy had been looking sad, too. She wished Mummy would hurry and talk to her so this bad feeling in her stomach would go away.

Marie was afraid.

Her mother came out and sat down beside her. She put her arm around her and smiled. "Don't look so frightened, Princess," she said. "Now let's talk about Karen."

"Tell me why she doesn't sit up and grab her rattle and kick her feet and crawl like John?"

"I'll tell you." Her mother spoke sweetly. "First, remember how good God was to send us a baby. Now the reason Karen cannot do these things is because God didn't make her arms and back and legs as strong as yours or John's or mine and she is not able to do the things that we do. What we need now is a doctor who can tell us how to help her to do these things. We will find one—I promise. It's a special kind of doctoring and Dr. John is helping. We will find one. Remember—I promise."

Marie's bad feeling went away. She was sad because her darling sister couldn't do these things but if Mummy promised to make everything come out all right, she wouldn't have that awful feeling any more. Her mother never broke a promise.

That evening when Marie and Mummy and Daddy said their night prayers together, as they always did, they added, "Please God, help Karen to use her hands and feet and to sit up."

CHAPTER FOUR

SEARCHING FOR THE DOCTOR

MANY times, now, Karen and her mother and father went away in the car. Marie missed them very much when they were gone, but she didn't mind because they were looking for a doctor who could tell them how Karen could use her hands and feet and sit up.

Once, when no one could come to stay with Marie, she went, too. It was great fun. She had Karen in her lap and held her up so she could see out the window. They saw cows, brown and white ones, which were all facing in the same direction. They saw pigs. These pigs were let out to pasture like cows and sheep, instead of being penned. They were pink and clean and shiny. In a pasture by a river Marie spotted a baby horse and three big horses.

"Daddy, stop—stop!" she called excitedly. "Let's go see the baby horse."

Daddy drove the car over beside the fence and stopped. "A baby horse is called a colt," he said as he opened the door. "Would you like to go over and talk to him?"

"Oh, yes, Daddy. Can Karen come too—and Mummy?"

"We'll all go," Daddy said. "But if you jump around or yell, you'll frighten him—so we'll tiptoe and whisper."

They tiptoed over to the fence, Daddy carrying Karen. The mother horse went over and stood close to her colt and watched them.

"I hope they won't run away," Marie whispered as she and Karen and Mummy and Daddy were as quiet as mice. Karen's eyes got rounder and rounder, for she had never seen a real live horse before. Cautiously they climbed up and sat on the fence. It was hard to sit so still but Daddy said if they did, the colt might come over to them. They waited and waited and then—HE DID! His legs were thin and long like sticks. They wobbled. Mummy said he was only four or five days old. He twitched his ears at them and then he shook himself a

little. They held their breath, for he was walking toward them. His mother came, too, as though she were afraid his shaky legs would buckle under his awkward steps. He walked right up to Marie and put his nose in her outstretched hand. She was so happy she wanted to squeal but she remembered just in time that it would scare him away. His nose was warm and so very soft. It felt just like her mother's black velvet hat. Karen laughed but surprisingly the noise didn't frighten the colt. Marie put Karen's hand on the soft, soft nose. They told him he was a good boy and very pretty. He tossed his head up and down.

"He's saying, 'Yes, I am,' " Marie told her father.

They didn't want to leave the colt ever but they had a long way to go before dark, so they all threw him kisses and promised to come back some day.

Soon Marie forgot about the colt because she was thinking about the doctor they were going to see and wondering if he could help Karen. Her mother and father were silent and she guessed they were probably thinking the same thing.

In spite of their wonderings, they made a gay adventure of the trip. They went across a big river on a boat that carried automobiles on it—a ferry. They got out of their car and stood at the rail. In the water all around them were other boats—big ones and little ones and medium sized ones, freshly painted ones and shabby ones. The boats had whistles that sounded like the big gold horn in the band. As the ferry moved out into the river the other boats blew their whistles to say, "Hello." The ferry blew its whistle back. It was the loudest of all. It said, "Here we come—get out of our way. *Woo-oo-oo-aa-aa-oo!*" And all the other boats obeyed the Big Whistle.

Later on in the afternoon, when the Killilea family were on the way home, a train whistled "Hello" to them as it went by and a man in a striped hat leaned out of the engine and waved. They all waved back and he blew the whistle again—"Good-bye."

Karen went to sleep but Marie snuggled down in her corner, wakeful until she could ask her mother and father a question. She wanted to ask and yet she was afraid, too.

"Mummy—what did the doctor say? Can he help Karen?" She hoped as hard as she could that her mother would say yes. She could play so many games with Karen if she could sit up.

Mummy answered slowly, "Not this time, dear. We'll try again—won't we Daddy?"

"You bet we will," Daddy assured her, and leaned over the back of the seat to pull the blanket around Marie. "Go to sleep, Princess."

"O.K.," Marie said drowsily and fell asleep thinking that her daddy could do anything.

Karen got fatter and fatter. She was completely round, with dimples in cheeks, elbows and knees.

Dr. John told Marie, "Karen is well and beautiful and plump because you take such good care of her. Because you give her so much love. Babies need love more than anything else to make them grow."

Marie was proud when he said this and even prouder when her mother told her father how Dr. John had praised her. Daddy observed, "That just shows how wise we were to make Karen your baby."

Marie was growing fast, too. Because she was good, she was happy. And because she was happy she was getting prettier and prettier. She took care of heating Karen's chopped food, and sometimes when Mummy had to go to the store she would leave Marie alone with Karen. So Marie was a "sitter" at an early age. She had a responsibility and this helped to make her happy.

Karen was now three years old and her sister felt very much like a mother when she had to scold her, as she sometimes did. Karen thought it lots of fun to try to whistle when she had a mouth full of food. The food would spurt out of her mouth—on her dress, on the tray, on the floor, on Marie. This was, of course, bad manners and, as a good mother, Marie *had* to scold. Karen, however, was such a joyous child that even when you scolded her, she laughed. Her laugh was "catching" and, as often as not, Marie had to laugh, too.

CHAPTER FIVE

A CHRISTMAS SURPRISE

"*CHRISTMAS* is coming! Christmas is coming." Marie put her arms around Karen and squeezed her hard. "Christmas is the most wonderful, exciting day in the whole year. We'll write a letter to Santa Claus and buy a great big tree—and eat lots of turkey—and get lots of presents—"

Marie and Mummy wrote a letter to Santa. Daddy took it to New York to mail it. Marie asked Santa for presents Karen would like. But she thought the best present would be a doctor who would help Karen use her arms and legs. Every time that Marie saw John running away from Kathy she wished Karen could run, too.

One bright afternoon, two weeks before Christmas, Marie and her mother went up to the attic. (They put Karen in the play pen and sat Denise beside her to keep her company.) Marie loved the attic. It had a tingly smell from the cedar wood and was filled with interesting boxes. These boxes had all kinds of surprises under their dusty covers.

Marie was specially delighted this day because they were going to do something they did only once a year. They were going up for the Christmas boxes. These were enchanting because they were filled with beauty for Jesus' Birthday. There were the tree lights—red, blue, yellow, green, all strung on green cord. There were bunches and bunches of silver tinsel. Some of the tinsel was so old it had turned to gold. Marie liked this best. So did her mother.

Way back in a corner was a pile of boxes that was taller than Marie. These had millions and trillions of ornaments in them. Every box had a label on it which told you just what was inside. Marie read the labels as her mother handed her the boxes. "Silver trumpets," "snowballs," "candy canes—make believe," "tiny balls for top of tree," "stars," "cornucopias," "angels' hair," "medium sized balls—all colors," "great big balls for lower branches—all colors," "little sleds with children on them," "reindeer," "Santa Clauses made of silk and stuffed," "Big Christmas stockings—for Mummy, Daddy, Marie, Karen," "strings of red and green beads and strings of colored paper made by Marie" (Mummy said these were the prettiest of all), "big SILVER STAR for tiptop of tree."

Marie always helped her mother and father put the lights and the tinsel on the tree, but the ornaments were left around the bottom for Santa to put on.

Marie and Mummy carried these boxes downstairs and Mummy said, "Now, for the best boxes of all." Her eyes were shining.

"Come on, Mummy—hurry!" cried Marie and her eyes were shining too.

"Hurry—hurry!" Karen repeated.

"We'll be right back, Sweetheart," Mummy told Karen. "Just wait until you see what is in the best boxes of all."

Marie and Mummy raced each other up the attic stairs. Marie won.

Way, way back in a corner was an old blue bureau. It had fairies' curtains on it. (Some people who don't know any better call them cobwebs.) Slowly, carefully, Marie and her mother opened the large middle drawer. Inside were white boxes tied with satin ribbons. Gently, they took them out and carried them downstairs. They placed them around Karen's play pen.

"Wait 'til you see, Karen." Marie was dancing with excitement. "Just wait! You'll love what's in these boxes—love them best of all."

Mummy watched while Marie untied the ribbons and took off the covers. Karen watched, too. Her eyes got rounder and rounder. Mother helped Marie take out wads of tissue paper and underneath there was:

A STABLE (a brown building made of wood—not quite like a house because it had only three sides and the front was open.)

BUNDLES OF STRAW

A COW

4 BIG WHITE SHEEP

8 LITTLE WHITE LAMBS

2 GRAY RABBITS

A SQUIRREL

A MOUSE

2 SHAGGY SHEEP DOGS

A CALF

A DONKEY

3 GOATS (with long beards)

A SHEPHERD DOG

A SHEPHERD BOY (with a red woolen coat)

A FATHER SHEPHERD

A LITTLE WOODEN BED (called a manger)

A BEAUTIFUL, BEAUTIFUL LADY (in a long blue cloak. She had golden hair and she was smiling.)

A HANDSOME MAN (in a brown robe. He had sandals on his feet. He was leaning on a staff. He looked proud and happy.)

AND—

THE LOVELIEST BABY THAT EVER WAS (The Baby was wrapped in soft white stuff. His chubby little arms reached out as though He was saying: "Come love me—I love you."

Karen said, "*Oh-o-o-ah-ah-ah*. Gimme!"

Marie laughed and said, "She thinks they're dolls."

"You tell her what they are," Mummy suggested. So Marie sat on the floor and her mother put Karen in her lap.

"Karen, honey," began Marie, "this is the *real* Christmas." She held up the figure of the Baby so Karen could see it. She kissed it. "This is the Baby Jesus. Christmas is His Birthday. That's why Christmas is all love." She picked up the figure of the beautiful lady and showed it to Karen. "This is His Mummy. Her name is Mary. She loves Him very much. She loves you very much, too. God made her more beautiful than any other lady."

Marie put the lady in Karen's arms and took up the figure of the handsome man. "And this is Joseph," she told her little sister. "He is Mary's husband and father to the Baby Jesus. He loves the Baby with his whole heart. He loves you, too. He took good care of Mary and the Baby."

Next, Marie picked up the Shepherd Boy. She went on, "One night this little boy was in a field with his daddy, watching his flock of sheep. They had these dogs to help them." And Marie put the two dogs beside Karen. "It was very cold," she continued "and they were shivering. All of a sudden—way, way up in the sky—a star began to shine—brighter and brighter. Then it grew bigger and bigger and bigger until the dark sky was all light. The Shepherd Boy and his daddy stood still and looked up in wonder. They didn't feel cold any more.

"While they were looking they heard wonderful music, soft at first, then it swelled and was joined with the most beautiful voices singing—and the Shepherd Boy and his daddy saw in the sky—angels. They could understand all the words as the angels sang, 'Glory to God in the Highest. Tonight a Baby is born in a stable. His name is Jesus. He is God become man. He is lying in a manger. Go and see Him.'

"So the Shepherd Boy and his daddy followed the star to a stable in Bethlehem. They took a birthday present to the Baby—one of the little white lambs. But they gave Him another present that the Baby liked better—they gave Him their love."

"So pretty," said Karen. "More."

"Now it's time to set up our crib," Mummy told her, gathering up the figures.

The Christmas scene was set up on a big long table. Marie and her mother made hills and valleys from books covered with a sheet and cotton and sprinkled with snow powder. They put pine branches around the stable for trees and made a little woods of them on the side of a hill. They sprinkled them with snow dust, too. They stood Mary and Joseph beside the manger and the cow and the donkey at the foot of the manger. The Shepherd Boy and his daddy were off in the field, hurrying toward the stable. The flock was grazing on the side of the hill while the dogs guarded them. The bunnies hopped across the snow to see the Baby, and the squirrel and the mouse shyly peeked around the corner of the stable. The goats walked slowly along the path, their heads turned toward the manger. Marie filled the manger with straw and then, most lovingly, placed the Baby with His arms outstretched to all the world.

Mummy was holding Karen up so she could watch all that was done and Karen kept saying, "Oh see, Mom. Oh see—pretty Baby."

Marie was thinking how happy they would all be if Karen could walk over to the crib and put out her hand and touch the Baby. Marie knelt down in front of the Baby and whispered softly so Karen couldn't hear, "Dear Baby Jesus, Christmas is Your Birthday. Couldn't *You* bring Karen a present? Please, please help Mummy and Daddy find a doctor who will teach Karen to use her arms and legs. Please, Baby. Thank you."

Just two days before Christmas Daddy said to Marie, "You're going to spend the day with Kathy and John. Mummy and I have found another doctor we want to see Karen."

"Will he help her, Daddy?" Marie asked hopefully.

"We don't know, Princess. We can only wait and see. We must keep looking and you must keep praying. If God wants her to walk, He'll help us find the right doctor."

"I will, Daddy, I will," Marie promised. "I'll ask Kathy to say a prayer, too, and maybe John, although he forgets to finish a prayer and starts blowing bubbles."

And Marie did pray. While she was playing with Johnny, while she was helping Mrs. Ruddy with the lunch dishes, while she was helping Kathy clean the silver.

She slept at the Ruddys' house that night but before breakfast the next morning she ran up the hill, hoping her mother and father had reached home. She was in such a hurry that she ran in the kitchen door, boots, snow and all. Karen was in her high chair and her mother and father were sitting at the kitchen table. When Mummy saw Marie she started to cry. Marie threw her arms around Mummy and squeezed her tight. Daddy put his arms around both of them.

"Princess, Princess," he said and his voice was shaking as if he were going to cry, too. "We found the doctor—we saw him yesterday.

Karen's going to sit up and use her hands and walk!!! He says she's very, very smart. Merry Christmas—Merry, Merry Christmas!"

And so it was that the Baby Jesus gave Karen *her* present for *His* Birthday.

CHAPTER SIX

WHY A NICKNAME?

MARIE had always hurried home from school to see Karen and then play games—hopscotch, jump rope, tag, king-of-the-hill, hide-and-seek, baseball. But now she hurried home faster than ever. She had a new Game to play and it was more fun than any of the others. It was the Game of teaching Karen to use her arms and legs.

One reason Marie liked this game best was because it was always played to music. There were all kinds of songs with pretty tunes and happy words.

Here is one

GALLOPY TROT

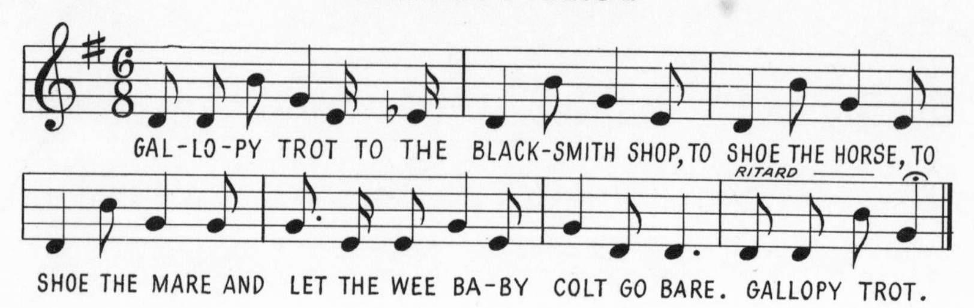

And here is another

BOBBY SHAFTOE

You can't play the Game but you can sing the songs.

One afternoon, the warm, sweet breath of spring made Marie skip all the way home from school. Mummy, who was ironing in the kitchen, asked, "Want some milk and cookies, Sweetheart?"

"Of course," answered Marie, taking off her jacket. "I'm always hungry. Will you fix the table for the Game?"

"I'll do it while you nibble."

Marie leaned over the play pen and kissed Karen and gave her a bite of her cookie. Then she sat on the kitchen stool and, through the doorway, watched her mother spread a blanket on the dining room table.

When everything was ready, Mummy picked up Karen, put her on

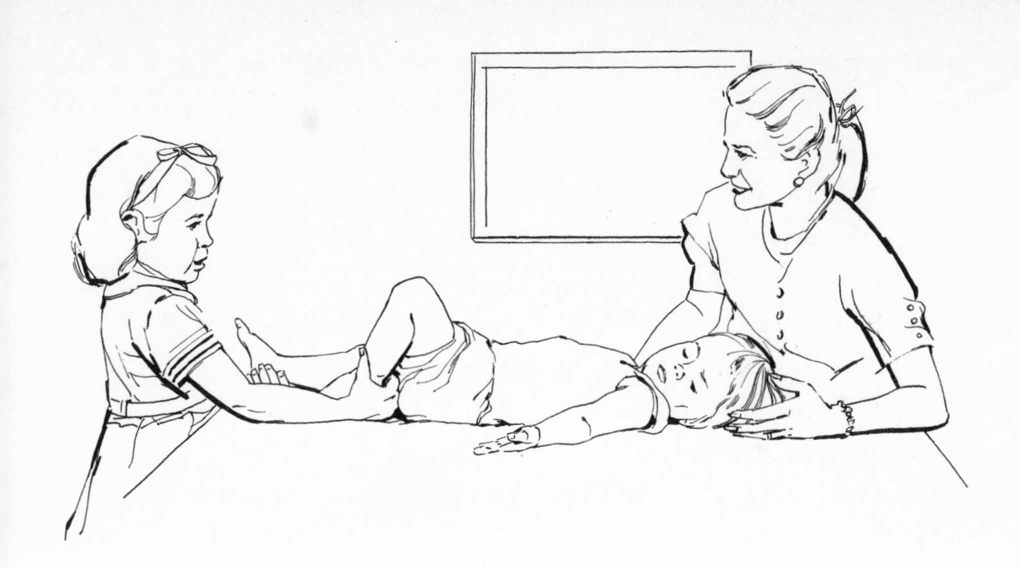

the table and took off her dress and slip, shoes and socks. Karen was lying on her back when Marie walked up to the foot of the table.

"Ready?" her mother asked.

"All ready," Marie said eagerly.

"You can have the first turn then." Mummy sat down beside the table.

Marie felt proud and important. She put her hands on Karen's ankles and said, just like Mummy did, "O.K. honey, make yourself all soft-soft-soft." And Marie made her voice soft when she said it. Karen's trouble was called cerebral palsy and it made her body stiff. In order to play the Game, she had to be relaxed—all over. "Make yourself all floppy like Raggedy Anne," Marie continued, always speaking softly. "Floppy and soft, for now you must be my rag doll." Karen watched Marie and *thought* away the stiffness until she was just like Raggedy Anne.

Marie started to sing *Gallopy Trot* and, in time to the music, she pushed Karen's ankles up, one at a time. Pushed them up to Karen's twiffy* and down. Up and down. Up and down. First one, then the other. Up and down. Push the foot, bend the knee, straighten the knee, pull the foot. This is exactly what you do every time you take a step. You knew how to do this when you were born. Karen had to be taught. What fun it was!

There was more to the Game than just the ankles. That would have grown dull. There were the knees, feet, back, hands, fingers. Marie and her mother had their turn in the daytime and Daddy played the Game at night. Karen learned the tunes quickly and often she and Daddy would whistle them when they weren't playing the Game.

Marie had wished for a long time that Karen could sit up so she could do more things with her. AND NOW SHE COULD. Of course, it had taken time, more than a year, and she couldn't do it all by herself—not yet. But her mother and father had a cute little chair made for Karen. It had a seat that tilted up in the front and down in the back. It had arms. There was a piece of wood at the bottom for Karen to rest her feet on. It was like the chairs that grown ups use in the yard or on the porch.

Marie thought she was the happiest little girl in the world. She probably was because she was helping someone.

Karen did some things slowly but once she started to talk—oh my! She talked fast and clear and used big words she heard adults use—and she talked most of the time.

It was when Karen was five that her family gave her a nickname. It was Wren. It fitted her perfectly.

A wren is a bird. He is tiny but courageous—so was Karen. He is a very friendly little creature. He is always happy and he trills beautifully. When he isn't trilling, he chatters, chatters, chatters. He likes an audience. He has bright eyes and when you talk to him, he listens with

**twiffy means bottom.*

his whole self. Even his pert little tail seems to be paying attention. But most of all he loves—he loves other birds (doesn't scrap like bluejays or sparrows). He loves the sun, he loves the rain, he loves flowers, he loves tiny bits of string, little sticks and, best of all, he loves his nest—him home—his family. So Wren was the perfect nickname for Karen.

When Wren chattered she called her mother "Mom Pom." She thought Mummy should have a nickname, too. Pretty soon many people were calling her mother Mom Pom and nearly everybody called Karen, Wren.

CHAPTER SEVEN

6 FOR MARIE—6 FOR WREN

THE Game was getting to be more fun every day because new and interesting things were added. Wren had been crawling for about six months and the doctor said it was now time for her to start to learn to walk. Believe it or not, he ordered SKIS to teach her!

The skis had a harness on the board to keep Wren's feet from slipping and there were upright poles in the front of each board. These she held as she stood, to help her keep her balance. When she first started to use them, Daddy and Mom Pom had to stand behind her and push the skis forward until Wren's muscles grew strong enough for her to do it herself. They sprinkled cornmeal on the floor

to make it slippery and it was just like sliding over snow. It looked like it, too. Marie's friends and Wren's friends used to argue over whose turn it was to use the skis when Wren was finished.

Because Wren's balance was still not very good, there was the chance that she would fall. If she fell, she probably would get hurt-unless she could be taught to fall properly. And it was in teaching Wren to fall that her family and friends had the most fun of all at the Game.

Daddy put a mattress in the middle of the living room floor. Then he and Mummy took turns showing the children how to fall without getting hurt. You do this by twisting your body, remembering to keep your head up and using your hands to break the fall. To show how it should be done, Daddy would invite Mom Pom to push him down. Then he would push her down. Then one of them would push Marie and pretty soon five or six yelling children would be shoving and pushing and falling. It was exciting and wonderfully noisy. After two or three weeks, Wren was falling as beautifully as any of her pals—and making just as much noise.

One evening, a couple of days after Easter, Mummy and Daddy and Marie and Wren were lying on the mattress. Wren's friends had gone home. The family was exhausted, for they had been playing the Game for over half an hour. Suddenly—there jumped up on the mattress a present that the Easter Bunny had brought. It was small and gray and furry. It was also fat. It had blue blue eyes and long long ears. It had a little black nose and a tail like the pompon on Marie's Scotch cap. And best of all—it was *alive.* It was a baby rabbit. Marie had named her Babbit.

"How did you think of that name?" her father had asked her.

"It was easy," Marie told him. "I just mixed up Bunny and Rabbit and it came out Babbit."

Babbit loved the Game as much as anyone but she loved it best when the family was on the mattress and she could play a game of her own. It was a combination of tag, hide-and-seek, dart and nibble. She particularly liked to play with the girls' braids (Wren's were almost as long as Marie's). Daddy caught Babbit and tossed her on Wren's neck. She hid there for a moment, then dashed right down the middle of Wren's back, giving her thin legs a sideways flick as she ran. The last time she had done this she had fallen head over heels off the side of the mattress. She had looked so surprised that Marie had run to get her camera but by the time she got back Babbit was off to some new mischief.

Now Babbitt sneaked around the edge of the mattress until she came to Daddy's shoe. She sat down—and she looked at the shoe—she looked at the lace. She bent her head, grabbed the lace in her teeth and started to tug. Daddy bent down, picked her up and put her on his head. She muzzled his hair for a little then slyly inched her way down his neck, under his chin, where she curled up and proceeded to nibble his necktie. While she nibbled she twitched her nose.

Marie said, "Just like Clare Newberry's Marshmallow," which was, if you remember, the name of the rabbit in the book she had been given for her birthday.

"Let's recite our favorite Marshmallow poem," Marie suggested. So the whole family began to chant:

A bunny nibbles all day long,
A bunny doesn't think it's wrong,
He nibbles mittens, mufflers, mops,
He only pauses when he hops.
He nibbles curtains, neckties, shoes,
He only stops to take a snooze.
Sofa pillows, ribbons, rugs—
He takes a mouthful, then he tugs.
Galoshes, boxes, books and string—
A bunny nibbles everything.
A bunny's a delightful habit.
No home's complete without a rabbit.*

Daddy built a nice house for Babbit. It was big and he filled it with fresh, sweet straw. It had a wooden back and sides, but the front was all glass. Mom Pom teased Daddy about the way he worked on Babbit's house. She was delighted when he put Wren and Princess to work on it, too. Wren sat in a chair (she didn't need the special one any more) and held nails. Daddy would hold a piece of wood in the right place and Marie would hammer.

This amused Mummy because she said, "Babbit lives in the house with us. Whatever does she need a house of her own for?"

**From "Marshmallow," by Clare Turlay Newberry (Harper & Brothers)*

Daddy chided her. "In the first place, Sweetheart, it is not called a house. It is called a hutch and some day she will have babies and then she will need it."

"Why?" asked Wren.

"Because," Daddy explained, "no one may touch a baby rabbit for at least a week after it is born."

One Sunday morning, in late summer, the family were all out in the yard, waiting for Daddy to drive them to church. He came out of the house with Babbit in his arms and walked over and put her in the hutch.

"Oh, Daddy, don't." Wren was almost crying. "She'll be lonesome."

"She really will, Daddy," said Marie.

"No she won't," her father said and looked mysterious. "You'll see."

Wren started to cry and Marie made a very disagreeable face and stamped her foot in temper. Her mother and father just looked at her.

"I'm going to let her out," stated Marie and walked over and put her hand on the latch.

"That, Princess, would be disobediance," said her father in a stern voice.

"I don't care," Marie retorted.

"If you think about it, I think you will," her mother said. "It would make Daddy and me very unhappy, but what is more important, it would make God unhappy. When you love Someone, you don't make Him unhappy."

Marie took her hand away. She bit her lip. She looked at her mother and father.

Her father said, "And it would be a bad example for Wren."

Marie leaned against the hutch and looked down at the ground. She still wanted to let Babbit out—but—she was on her way to God's house and she decided she couldn't make Him unhappy and then visit

Him. That would be the most awful kind of rudeness. And—God would think she didn't love Him.

Marie sighed a big sigh. Mother looked at her and smiled. "Never mind, Darling. Being good because you love God is often hard. It's hard for grownups, too. But you'll never be sorry—that I promise you."

Marie and Wren gave Babbit a final kiss and a pat and went off to church. As soon as they were back home they all hurried to the hutch to tell her they were going to take her into the house and they hoped she hadn't missed them too much. But Babbit was not alone. She was lying down and beside her and around her were *twelve baby bunnies!*

CHAPTER EIGHT

DEMON OR ANGEL

WREN got another big assist in her walking. She got braces. She did much better than on her skis and Marie began to wonder if the time might come when Wren might walk with crutches. Marie and Wren loved to polish and shine the braces.

The braces were especially helpful because they had joints in the metal just where we have joints in our legs. This made it easy to move in them.

Mummy and Daddy did quite a bit of bragging about how much Marie had done for Karen. They were also pretty proud of their Wren who worked so hard, never showed discouragement, never complained.

"She does her very best in everything," said Mom Pom. "That's why she accomplishes so much."

Mummy did get really cross if anyone did too much for Wren. She had to scold Marie many times for this. It was hard for Marie not to do certain things for her sister, she loved her so. But Mummy was very firm on this, as was Daddy.

"Karen must learn to do things for herself, even if it's difficult," Mummy explained. "It is certainly no kindness to do things for her when it means she would not learn to do them for herself. Only by doing things for herself can she become independent. Karen is no different from any child. All children should learn to be independent. They must learn to depend on themselves as far as they are able."

It was hard for Marie to watch her Wren struggle fifteen minutes to put on her slip when she could do it for her in half a minute. But she did the hard thing because she loved Wren and it was good for her sister.

Karen quickly became proud of her independence and she would say to anyone who wanted to help her do something that she could do alone, "Let me alone, thank you, I can do it myself."

Marie and Wren were playing records one Saturday afternoon when there was a knock on the door. Mummy and Marie stopped dancing and Daddy went to see who was there. It was Frank Bruckner, an old friend. He was a big jolly person and loved children, so every-

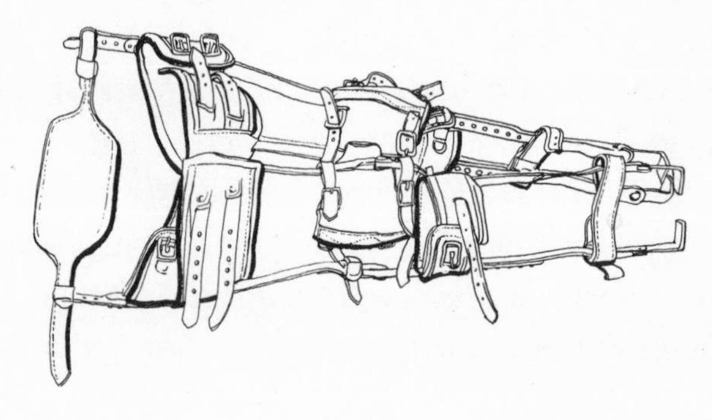

one was glad to see him. He took off his hat and coat and walked over to Karen.

"Hello, Wren," he greeted her and planted a big kiss on the tip of her nose.

"Gee, I'm glad to see you," Karen told him.

"You'll be even gladder when you see what I have for you." And he looked most mysterious.

"A present?" asked Wren hopefully.

"A very special present. It's for you but it will make the whole family happy. Guess."

"Give me a hint first."

"Well—let me see. It's large and sort of red and can make different kinds of noises."

"A big fire truck?"

"Nope. Guess again."

Wren thought hard. "I just can't think of what it could be. Did you bring it with you?" And she looked around to see if there was something she hadn't noticed.

"Yes, I did. He's in the car."

"He?" She was looking more and more puzzled. "Oh, please go get it—or him. I can't wait!"

Mummy and Daddy were looking at each other wisely, so Wren knew they were in on the secret. "Do you know what it is?" she asked Marie.

"No," said Marie in a voice tight with excitement, "and I wish he'd hurry. I can't wait either."

Frank Bruckner was out and back in no time at all. He walked in the door, pulling something behind him. When the children saw what it was they screamed. It was an Irish setter puppy.

"Meet Tam O'Shanter of Knightscroft." Frank was grinning as he

saw Marie's and Karen's joy. He slipped the leash and the pup was off like a shot. Daddy ran over to stand beside Wren, who was on her skis, to protect her just in case this violent creature should run into her. Tam O'Shanter of Knightscroft tore around the room—he knocked over a table—he crashed into a chair—he leapt into Mummy's lap and licked her face and jumped down and dove at Marie. She tried to get her arms around him but he wriggled away and ran over to her father. Daddy tried to quiet him but with no success. Then the pup turned and headed at breakneck speed straight for Wren. But—instead of hurling himself at her as he had at everything and everyone else, he stopped short and *walked* around her. He licked her hand. He was quiet as a mouse. Then he dashed off again.

"Well, what do you think of that?" asked Daddy in a tone of awe.

"I wouldn't believe it if I hadn't seen it," Mom Pom said.

"I told you he was the smartest pup I've ever had," Frank told them.

"I believe it." And Daddy looked at the dog in amazement.

"Frank," said Karen, and her eyes were shining, "I can't ever, ever thank you. I'd rather have that puppy than anything in the whole wide world."

Marie's eyes were shining, too. "So would I." And she ran to Frank and gave him a big squeeze and a kiss.

"Come, let me kiss you, too," said Karen. "I love you," she whispered as Frank bent for her kiss.

Finally the pup fell exhausted at Karen's feet. Now they could get a good look at him. His coat was long, silky and shiny. It was the color of bright mahogany. His feathers (those are the long hairs on the under part of the belly, throat, and on the legs) were long and full—not curled. (A good setter does not have curly feathers.) He looked awkward; since he was growing up, his legs seemed too long for his body. The shape of his head was perfect and his eyes were a soft brown, like chocolate candy left too long in the sun. He was perfect.

Well, not exactly perfect if you consider his behavior, for Tam O'Shanter of Knightscroft was so rambunctious that in the first two weeks he broke four lamps (only the really nice ones that Mummy and Daddy had received as anniversary presents), ate six books, smashed a coffee table and five quart bottles of milk. Just when Mummy was ready to strangle him or ship him back to Frank with her compliments, he'd do something especially sweet. Like sitting in front of Wren and putting his head on her knee and looking up at her as though he worshipped her, which he did. Because of his mischief, he was not called Tam O'Shanter of Knightscroft, but Shanty Irish. And Shanty Irish he stayed.

What the family did not know at first was that Wren had acquired a second guardian angel. From the very start Shanty was careful of her but as time went on, he took charge of her. She could go nowhere without him. When Mummy said, "Time for your nap, Wren," Shanty would get up and walk with them to the bed and then curl up at the top where the person should be. Wren would sleep with her head on his shoulder. He wouldn't move until she awakened.

CHAPTER NINE

A STEP FORWARD—AND UNDER

THERE was a young girl in the neighborhood named Gloria Kyle. She was exceptionally pretty and ever so sweet. She came to the house now and then to stay with the children if Mummy and Daddy were going out, and often, after school, she visited just to play with them. They grew to love her very much. So did Mummy and Daddy. So did Shanty. So did the bunnies.

As time went on Gloria was at the house some time during almost every day. It was she who thought of a new part of the Game that would help Wren's hands. She bought a set of finger paints and taught the children how to use them.

One afternoon she put on a contest for all the children in the neighborhood.

"You be the judge," she told Wren's mother, "and you, Marie, fill

the roasting pans with water to soak the papers in."

"How about some prizes?" Mummy asked.

"Wonderful!" chorused the children.

"Good—we'll have four first prizes," Mummy promised. "A box of lollypops, a package of balloons and some trading cards and marbles."

The children really worked and when they were through they put their papers on the kitchen walls. It is certain they made a frightful mess but Mummy didn't mind a bit. She judged the paintings for The Most Original, The Most Colorful, The Most Artistic, The Funniest.

Marie and Wren did not win a prize but Wren got something even more important. From doing a lot of finger painting, her hands began to work better and her use of a fork and spoon improved greatly. She could handle toys and as time went on she became adept at turning the pages of a book.

Her father took her fork and spoon and bent the handles so that they were easier to hold.

Her mother made a "button board." Marie and Gloria and Mummy and Wren used to work on this for hours and hours. It was all part of the Game and always fun.

And under the cloth Mummy used to put new and beautiful pictures, so that each time Wren opened the buttons there was something interesting or exciting beneath. This was a big help to Wren in learning to dress herself, for no one can dress himself if he cannot button buttons. There was also a zipper board.

One night, as usual, Daddy lifted Wren up into her chair for dinner. Gloria was there and she was telling a silly joke when the telephone rang. The family were in the dining room and the phone was in the kitchen.

"I'll get it," Wren sang out.

This was a really good joke because she coudln't walk to the kitchen. She couldn't walk alone at all.

Father laughed and said, "Don't run. You might break a leg."

Wren shrieked with laughter—"And then I couldn't walk."

At that remark, everyone laughed and laughed. Not just because it was a good joke, but because Wren had made the joke on herself. Gloria laughed so hard she started to choke and Daddy had to get up and pat her on the back.

Later, when Wren had been tucked in bed and the family had finished their night prayers, Marie asked Mummy and Daddy a question that worried her a great deal. She was happy as could be about all the progress Karen made, but—"Will Wren walk by herself —*ever?*"

"With her hard work and the help of all of us and prayer, we hope that one day she will be able to use crutches," Mummy answered.

"Oh, Mom Pom, really?"

"Really."

"When?"

"We mustn't be impatient, Princess," Daddy warned her. "It will take time—maybe a long, long time."

"When it happens, won't Shanty love it?" Marie looked at the Irish setter as he lay in front of the crackling fire. "He and Wren can go off all by themselves." Shanty opened one eye and wagged his tail. Two of the bunnies pounced on it.

Marie went on, "Kathy was bragging today about how well John roller skates."

"He does skate well. It's unusual for a child his age," said Mummy.

"Well, when she was bragging about Johnny, I bragged about Wren."

"Oh?" queried Daddy. "And what did you say?"

"I said she had a better vocabulary than most adults and if she ever started using her big words with Kathy, she wouldn't know what Wren was saying. Sometimes I don't," Marie half-whispered, "but I didn't tell Kathy that."

"Humph!" grunted Daddy.

"Is that kind of bragging wrong?" Marie looked a little worried.

"Well—" Daddy started.

"No," Mom Pom said positively.

"No," repeated Daddy, smiling at Mummy.

"I'm glad." Marie nodded her head. "You know something? The other day when Wren and I were having lunch at Ruddy's, John was acting up something awful and Wren told him 'John, I am appalled at your barbaric behavior.' I had to stop and think about what she meant."

"I should think so," Mummy agreed, chuckling.

Marie walked over to Daddy and put her arm around his neck. "Tomorrow's Saturday," she said, "and you don't go to the office. Can we all go swimming?"

"*May* we," Mummy corrected.

"May we?" Marie repeated.

"It's a date," Daddy told her.

"Gee, I hope it doesn't rain." Marie looked suspiciously at the few little clouds in the sky.

The next morning she woke to find the sun striking sparkles from everything it touched. The family hurried with breakfast and the dishes and the beds and the Game and by ten o'clock they were at the beach. Gloria went, too.

Marie had learned to swim before she could walk and went fishing before she could talk, but Mummy and Daddy realized that it would be some time before Karen could swim. They thought, however, that this summer they could take her along when they went fishing. Daddy felt that this would not be safe unless Wren knew how to hold her breath when under water. So—he decided to teach her.

There were only a few people and some noisy gulls on the beach when they arrived. Gloria and Marie raced right into the water, swimming, chasing each other and playing "Dead-Man's Float." Daddy picked up Karen. "Come on, Wren, we're going to have a lesson."

"What kind of a lesson, Daddy?"

"A lesson in holding your breath under water."

"You mean when I'm submerged?"

Mom Pom hid a smile behind her hand. "Yes—when you're submerged."

They ran to the water's edge. Mom Pom had brought a bag of brightly colored marbles. Daddy placed Wren on her stomach on the water's edge. He took five or six marbles and put them in the water within her reach. "Now, sweetheart," he told her, "you are going to pick up the marbles and hand them to Mummy."

"O.K., Daddy."

When Wren had picked these marbles up, her father put some more in the water, only this time out deeper. Wren had to crawl into the water so she could reach them. The little waves slapped over her and she called to Gloria and Marie, "Hey, look at me! I'm having a lesson." The girls came over to watch.

A big wave came along and washed into Karen's face. She sputtered and coughed. "Now, Wren," Daddy told her, "this is the lesson. When the water reaches your face—hold your breath. That way you won't inhale any. We'll practice and practice until after a while you can hold your breath for a long time."

Marie threw herself down beside Wren, and put her face close to the water. "Like this," she said and pulled in a big breath and held it while the water washed over her face. "Then like this," she said and blew her breath out.

A few more waves, a few more sputterings and coughings and suddenly Karen caught on. She'd reach for a marble and when she saw a wave coming, she'd breathe in deep and fast and hold her breath until the wave was gone.

"You're pretty smart." Her mother sounded proud. She turned and dove into the water. She swam out and back, coming up to Karen like a seal, swimming first on top of the water and then swimming under the water so Wren didn't know where she was. She made noises like a seal, that sounded like the blare of a rusty trumpet.

"I want to do that, Mom Pom," Wren said.

"You'll do it sooner than you think,"' Mummy assured her, "now that you're learning to hold your breath."

For the next two weeks Karen went "swimming" every day and every day she practiced.

It was Saturday and Wren was picking up the marbles quite well.

Her father was putting them out deeper and deeper. In order to pick them up now, Wren had to put her face closer and closer to the surface of the water. Then Daddy took a huge blue marble that Karen loved and put it in quite deep water. Mummy and Marie and Gloria were watching intently because they knew that Wren would have to put her face *under* the water to get it.

"Come on, Honey," said Marie, "get it quick before it moves away."

Four times Wren put her face down and reached for it, but she pulled back each time she felt the water on her whole face.

"You pick it up, Mom Pom."

"Not on your life," Mummy answered. "If you want it, you must get it."

Wren looked at Daddy and Gloria and Marie.

"You can do it," they told her in unison.

"Then I will," said Wren. She looked at the marble, sucked in a deep breath, put her head down and *under.* One second, two—she pulled her head back, blew out her breath and held out the blue marble to show them.

"You did it! You did it!" they all sang out. "You're wonderful!"

Karen was beaming. "I'll do it again," she said. "It's not hard—it's fun." And without waiting for Daddy to put another marble under the water, she ducked her head and came up with a pebble. She did it over and over again.

"Everything looks pretty under water, Daddy," she said. "I want to come tomorrow and practice some more."

By the end of the next week, for Mummy took her every day, Wren could hold her breath under water as long as Marie and Gloria and Mummy and Daddy.

CHAPTER TEN

A SERIOUS ACCIDENT

MARIE enjoyed this summer very much because Wren could do so many more things. But as she watched her sister she often had a little catch in her heart—wondering "Will she ever be able to walk?"

Karen was as busy as could be. Besides all the exciting parts of the Game, she had twelve bunnies to care for. Shanty cared for them, too. Apparently he didn't think Babbit got them clean enough because he washed them and washed them. They were tiny and his tongue was big and long and often when he was licking them he'd push them several inches along the floor. Once, when one was lying on a chair, he licked her right through the spokes and she bounced on the floor. But the bunnies didn't seem to mind and would chase Shanty around the house and tease him dreadfully by nibbling on his feathers or ears

when he was trying to sleep. They were not the least bit afraid of him.

The two things that Wren and her friends enjoyed most were:

Playing the Game with their dolls (they called this therapy), they would put their dolls on the bench in the yard and move their legs and arms and backs just as Marie did to Wren.

The second favorite game was playing house with the bunnies.

Deciding on names for twelve bunnies had not been easy, but finally it was done. They were: Flopsy, Mopsy, Cotton-Tail, Peter, Black Mumbo, Black Jumbo, Little Black Sambo, Prancer, Dancer, Dasher, Comet, and Blitzen.

The youngsters would dress the bunnies in doll's clothes, including little bonnets, and then put eight or ten of them in the doll carriage. Marie would push Wren's wheel chair (which Daddy had bought so she could go everywhere) and Karen would lean forward and push the carriage.

The children would fix meals for the bunnies, too—carrot tops, celery, radishes and, of course, bits of cucumber. They'd put these on a little low table and the bunnies would sit up on their hind legs and eat almost like a person. All the while they ate, their whiskers would twitch.

When they'd had enough, they'd jump down and dash away, then turn in a circle, kicking up their hind legs, and dash back again.

One night at dinner, Mummy said to Daddy in a worried voice, "Daddy, I think you'd better call the exterminator."

"Why?" asked Daddy as he cut Wren's meat. (She couldn't do this alone yet.)

"Well," said Mummy and she acted embarrassed, "I think I'm a good housekeeper and keep the rugs clean—but we must have moths."

"I haven't seen any," said Daddy.

"I haven't either," Mom Pom told him. "But look at the bare spots in the rugs."

Marie and Wren looked at each other and burst out laughing.

"I don't see anything funny about it," Mummy said crossly.

They laughed harder.

"Children!" Their father's voice was sharp with displeasure.

"But—Daddy—" Wren gasped, the tears running down her cheeks from her laughter.

Daddy stood up. He was very angry.

Marie and Wren didn't often see their father angry so they stopped laughing.

Marie said, "We must have moths in the piano legs, too—" And the two girls started laughing all over again.

Daddy was very red in the face. He looked at Mummy and then suddenly sat down and began to laugh, too. Now it was Mummy's turn to look angry.

"Mom Pom," Daddy's eyes began to water as he roared with mirth, "don't you *see?*"

"I don't see anything," said Mummy in a hurt voice.

Daddy tried to stop laughing enough to talk. "You don't have moths–" he choked over the words "you have BUNNIES–bunnies that eat rugs and piano legs!!"

Mom Pom looked startled for a moment–then laughed as boisterously as they. "This must stop," she said finally, wiping her eyes. "Oh, my–what next?"

"A snake," suggested Wren.

"NO!" said Mummy and Daddy together.

The bushes and trees were wearing their bright fall outfits of orange, brown and crimson. Daddy said, "Let's visit the Healys' this afternoon and go for a ride on their lake."

Ethel Healy and Mummy were the same age, and so were Sherman Healy and Daddy. Their brother, Jay, was a little older. They lived with their mother, a darlin' mite of an Irish lady. The Healys were old friends and loved all the Killileas, including Shanty.

It was a perfect day for boating. The Healys' cousin Bill was visiting, and as there were too many for one boat, Bill took Karen and Marie in the rowboat and Jay and Ethel and Mummy and Daddy went in the canoe. Sherman stayed home to finish a picture he was painting. Mrs. Healy said she would fix tea while they were gone.

The canoe followed about fifty feet behind the rowboat. Marie was sitting on the seat beside Wren, with her arm around her. Wren was dragging a stick in the water.

Marie called to Mummy, "Let's go in near the island. Wren and I want to watch the fish under the water and play hide-and-go-seek under the weeping willow trees."

"All right," Mom Pom answered, and turned to look at the island. A moment later Daddy dove over the side of the canoe into the water. The rowboat was behind a willow and Mummy couldn't see the children but she knew something must have happened. She stood up and dove in, too—upsetting the canoe as she did so and dumping Jay and Ethel into the lake. When she came to the surface, she saw Bill with his arm around Marie but Wren was not in the boat! Mummy knew then that Daddy had seen Karen fall overboard. She swam after him to the rowboat and saw him dive down. She dove down, too, looking for Wren who couldn't swim. Mummy dove three times without finding her, praying over and over, "Please, God, help us find her."

Daddy stayed under the water until he thought his lungs would burst for want of air—and then—he saw his Wren. He grabbed her and swam back up to the surface.

Mummy saw them and swam over to them, murmuring, "Thank you, God. Thank you very much."

Together Mummy and Daddy got Wren over the side and into the rowboat and clambered in after her. Bill and Marie were holding her. She was pale but she didn't even cough.

Marie was very pale, too. She clung to Karen tightly—terribly frightened still. Her face looked frozen. "I couldn't help it, Mom Pom, honestly I couldn't." Marie started to cry with big deep sobs.

"I'm sure you couldn't, Sweetheart," Mom Pom said.

Marie's words tumbled out between sobs. "She was dragging that s-stick—and d-dropped it in the water. She lunged over the side after it. I couldn't hold her. I really couldn't. And—and—she went over." She sobbed and sobbed.

"Your thinking was quick and good, Princess," Daddy told her. "It was an accident. You weren't careless—it was an accident that nobody could stop."

"Wren's all right—aren't you, Wren?" Mom Pom looked lovingly at the precious little girl.

"I'm perfectly all right, Honey." Wren smiled at Marie. "Please don't cry any more. I'll tell you something. You know—it was pretty down there. While I was waiting for Daddy I held my breath and looked around. I'll tell you all about it if you stop crying."

"I—'ll—try," Marie choked back a sob and sniffled. "But you do know I—I couldn't help it—don't you, Wren?"

"I know, Sweetheart—I know," said her sister and patted her cheek.

On the way home Daddy stopped the car at church and they all went in and said, "Thank you." They looked very funny, dressed up in Jay's and Sherman's and Ethel's clothes—just like Halloween, but they knew God would understand and be glad to see them.

CHAPTER ELEVEN

THE MENAGERIE GROWS

THERE were several additions to the Killilea menagerie that Spring. Two cats, a canary and—of all things—a mother and father wren who built a house in the feeding station in the large tree outside the kitchen window.

The cats arrived first. Shanty loved them from the start. They were a present from the Balfes, friends of Mummy's and Daddy's. Mom Pom said the Balfes were very intelligent, since they appreciated and understood cats. They presented the Killileas with two Maine coon cats. These cats have a long, rich, silky coat, very much like a combination Persian and Angora. They were first brought to Maine by seamen on vessels coming from the Orient. Due to the cold climate, these cats flourished in Maine.

The male, the Killileas named Sandy McTavish—he looked so like a debonair Scotsman. Marie and Wren did a lot of arguing over what they should call the female. Mom Pom listened to their wrangling for several days and decided to settle the matter herself and restore peace. "*I* shall name the cat," she told them. "Henceforth she shall be called 'Anonymous.' "

"That's a queer name." Marie was puzzled.

"What does it mean?" Wren wanted to know.

"You can call her Nonny for short—it means bearing no name."

"That's cute," said Wren, "and it gives me a new word for my vocabulary. The next time I'm naughty and you ask me who did the mischievious thing I shall say anonymous, but I won't mean the cat."

"I like it," said Marie.

"That's fine," Mummy told them, "then there'll be no more arguing."

The next arrival was the bird—a canary. It was no problem to know what to call him. In a manner of speaking, he named himself. The first day they had him, he ducked his head and almost bent himself in half, to get into his water cup to take a bath. So they called him Dunk. He was not timid and the noisier the house, the better he liked it. His feathers were a rich yellow, fading out to a paler tone at the tips of his wings. At the end of two weeks he was eating off their fingers and "fighting" with them. They would put his cage on the table after dinner and take turns fighting. Wren would go first. She would move her face slowly up to the cage, make a furry sound and then move her head slowly from side to side. Dunk would hunch his head down between his shoulders, spread his wings, open his beak and *attack*. Wren would move her head around and he would follow from perch to perch, making little make believe angry noises. Then she'd hold still with her nose between the bars and he would assault her, pecking her nose and scolding at the same time. But he never really hurt.

They had a little trouble with Shanty the first day or two after the canary came. When Dunk started to sing (his voice was angelic) Shanty would stand still and "point." He would look like a statue, head slightly lowered, right forepaw up, tail straight out behind. Daddy took a firm hand with Shanty, not knowing what might follow his "point." It was natural that the dog should do this, since Irish setters have been trained for many generations to hunt birds. After a while Dunk would try to "fight" with Shanty—but somehow Shanty never got the hang of the game. He'd sniff, lick the cage and set it swinging, then walk away.

The whole family had to take a firm hand with Sandy McTavish and Nonny, too. It was more than a month before the cats stopped stalking Dunk and licking their chops when they passed his cage.

Then came the wrens. Because of Karen's nickname, they were of special interest. The children watched them set up housekeeping. The father wren seemed to do all the work. The mother wren was busy, too —but not working. She followed her mate around to see that he did a good job, and she coaxed and scolded and talked the whole time. (Daddy said the male was "wren-pecked".) This busy male wren picked up sticks and bits of grass and pieces of string that Mom Pom put on the lawn and carried them back to the nest. In the evening, when their day's work was done, the friendly birds would follow whoever was out in the yard. They'd flit from tree to tree and carry on a conversation. And at some time during every evening, they gave a concert.

Daddy said, "If there's anything sweeter than the song of a wren, I don't know what it is."

One morning, Daddy started off for his train. A few minutes later he came hurrying back into the house. "Quick," he picked up Karen, "everybody out in the yard—we have baby wrens."

They all rushed out and stood under the feeder, turned birdhouse. "Listen, now," said Daddy. They stood quietly and listened. Soon they heard little, tiny, thin peepings. The mother bird flew out and in a few minutes was back with something in her mouth. She flew in to the babies and the peepings grew louder as they demanded their breakfast.

"Oh, I can't wait to see them," said Marie.

"Neither can I." Wren was staring at the wren's house as though she could see through the wooden walls.

"I'm going to be late for work." Daddy handed Wren to Mummy and dashed down the hill.

One evening, about three weeks later, the family went out to listen to the baby wrens. As they stood beside the tree Mom Pom said, "I hope everything is all right. I haven't heard the big ones since yesterday morning." Daddy looked startled. They whistled and called but the mother and father bird were nowhere to be seen. They stood a long time, listening for the chirpings of the little ones, but there was no sound.

Daddy said, "Something is wrong." He fetched a ladder and put it against the tree. He climbed up to the birdhouse. Wren kept looking all around, hoping the mother and father would come back. Daddy put his ear against the hole in the front of the house and listened. He shook his head. Very carefully and very slowly he put his finger in the hole and moved it around inside. He took it out, just as slowly, and came down the ladder. He looked upset. "The little ones are in there," he told the anxious watchers, "but I'm afraid something has happened to the mother and father. I'm not sure the little ones are alive."

"Oh-oh-oh!" Karen wailed. "What shall we do?"

"Take them out, Daddy," Marie suggested. "Maybe we can help them."

Gloria came up the hill just then and they told her of the tragedy. "Oh, do take them out," she begged. "Maybe we can save the little ones."

"All right," Daddy said, "I'll try." He went for a big pair of shears and climbed back up the ladder. He cut the rope and handed the birdhouse to Mummy. She steadied it while he worked the nails out and took the front off. There, inside, were six tiny birds. They were very still. Wren put her finger tenderly on top of one. "Oh, Mom Pom, he's cold!" And she started to cry.

Mom Pom touched the baby wrens one after the other. "I'm afraid they're dead," she said in a low voice.

"There must be *something* we can do." Marie was crying now.

"Let me think," said Mummy. She thought and thought. "Well, I can try," she said to herself and turned to Daddy. "Bring the birdhouse into the kitchen," she said. She picked up Karen and went indoors, followed by all the others. Daddy put the house on the kitchen table. Mummy went over and lit the gas stove oven on a low heat. Next she went to the closet for a pie tin. Then she went to the birdhouse and took out the babies, nest and all. She put them on the pie tin and put the tin in the oven, leaving the door open. The family sat on the floor in front of it. They sat quite a long time, watching, and then suddenly one of the tiny creatures moved its head. They held their breaths. After a little, another moved and then another. An hour later, five baby wrens had revived. The six they put in a cardboard box that Mummy's earrings had come in (that's how tiny he was) and buried him in the yard. They had a funeral procession and sang Brahm's *Lullaby* very softly and sadly. Then they put some dandelions on the grave and went back into the house.

Marie and Gloria made a new nest for the others of cotton in a cup. They put the five bird babies in it and covered them over, except for their heads. "However are we going to feed them?" Mummy asked Daddy.

"I wish I knew," he told her anxiously.

"Let me think," said Mom Pom for the second time. She walked up and down the kitchen, thinking. "They'll die if I don't think of something soon," she murmured to herself. The children sat quietly so they wouldn't interrupt her thinking. She murmured some more—then—"I'll try it!" she exclaimed. "If I don't, they'll die anyway."

Mummy hurried upstairs and came back with a pair of eyebrow tweezers. She put some milk on the stove to heat and took out a box of pablum. She broke an egg into a bowl. She beat the egg and added one drop of vitamin oil, then some pablum and warm milk and beat the mixture well. With the tweezers she picked up a mite of the mixture and carried it over to the birds. First she tapped a little beak. Nothing happened. It stayed tight shut. She tapped it lightly again and

then the beak flew open and the wee one made a faint chirp.

"His mouth is so big!" Marie exclaimed. "It's about as big as all the rest of him."

"It's enormous," Karen agreed.

Meanwhile Mom Pom was working the mixture off the tweezer on the inside of the beak. The beak closed and they all waited anxiously. The baby moved his head a little, opened his beak a fraction, moved his tongue and swallowed. They waited. Mummy put some more of the mixture on the tweezer and tapped the beak again. It opened and she put the food into the hungry mouth. Again the bird swallowed it.

"He's eating—he's eating—he's ravenous—he's going to live!" Wren fairly yelled, in her relief.

"You can't be sure," Daddy tried to keep her from getting too happy. He didn't want her disappointed.

"I'm sure they'll all live." Wren had no doubts.

"We all hope so," said Gloria, "but it will take several days before we can be sure."

"May I feed them, Mom Pom?" Marie asked.

"You'll all have turns tomorrow," Mom Pom promised. "But tonight I think I'd better do it."

"I think they haven't eaten in a day or more," Daddy said as he watched the beaks open hungrily, one after the other. "Oh, my hat!!"

"What's the matter?" Mummy asked. "Did I do something wrong?"

"No," Daddy told her. "What you're doing is right but I just thought of how often you are going to have to do it."

"I've already thought of it." Mummy didn't look bothered.

"They're going to have to be fed every two hours day and night until they get their strength back."

"Well, how in the world are we going to manage that?" Daddy wanted to know.

"Just the way we did with the children and the night bottles," Mom Pom told him calmly. "We'll take turns."

"*Who'll* take turns?" Daddy asked suspiciously. "The children can't get up at night."

"No, darling," Mummy smiled sweetly, "but you and I can."

Daddy looked horrified. "Taking shifts to feed a baby is one thing. You know I enjoyed that. But shifts for feeding birds is something else again." He looked around to find one sympathetic face. No one said a word or looked in the least sympathetic. He began to feel uncomfortable. "After all," he went on rather weekly, "I have to go to work—and—and—" He was now appealing to Wren and Gloria and Marie. They looked a little shocked—as though he were failing them. He cleared his throat. They continued to stare at him. "Oh, well," he said in a voice of forced joy, "it will really be fun—and it won't be for long."

"Daddy, you're a darling!" exclaimed Wren.

"I knew you'd do it," Marie told him and ran over and kissed him.

"So did I," said Mummy and went over to turn off the oven.

CHAPTER TWELVE

FUN, TROUBLE, AND ANOTHER GIFT

THE yard was always filled with children. Daddy thought of wonderful things that children liked. For instance—he got an old automobile tire and hung it by a long, strong rope from the branch of a tree. It made the best swing ever. The tree was on the side of the hill so when the children really got swinging, they would sail out into space. It was thrilling. Wren loved it.

Shanty hated it.

When Marie would put Wren in the tire she would tie a big cloth around her sister's waist and the tire so she couldn't slip. Marie watched Karen carefully while she was swinging and never pushed her too high. But Shanty disapproved of the whole business. He thought it was wrong for *his* little girl to go sailing out into space—and he said so.

As soon as Marie would pick Wren up and put her in the tire, Shanty would start to bark, and he continued to bark until Wren was taken off. But that wasn't all he did. While Marie was tying Karen on, Shanty would move around in front of the tire and plant himself firmly. He'd grown a greal deal and was now a big and strong dog. (Frank Buckner said Shanty was the biggest setter he'd ever seen.) He'd push his feet hard on the ground and make his legs stiff. Then he'd bark as if to say, "You can't push Wren with me standing right in front of the tire. I won't move. I won't let you push her."

Mom Pom or Daddy or Gloria would talk to him and explain that they wouldn't permit the swinging if it weren't safe. He'd pay no attention. They'd tell him to move. Ordinarily he was very obedient—but he'd refuse to move an inch. Then they'd take hold of his collar and pull. He'd stiffen his back and legs and they couldn't move him. So, in order for Wren to have her swing, two people would have to work on Shanty. One would pull and the other would push from behind. Barking furiously in protest, he would be dragged away.

Once Mummy and Daddy tried locking him in the house while they took Wren to the tire. He promptly went through the window, shattering glass, frame and all. He was hopeless—but every one in the family loved him the more for his devotion to Wren.

He took such good care of her that Mummy could leave Wren in his charge and wash and iron and make beds and clean the house without taking Karen from room to room with her. Shanty had two warning barks. One was short and sharp and told Mom Pom that Wren had fallen. Then Mummy would go and help her up. The other was strong and angry and Shanty used it if Wren was out in the yard and someone strange came over to her. Daddy said there was no governess in the whole wide world he would trade for this red-haired, four-footed guardian angel.

One evening, the family sat in the dining room after dinner, watching the cats chase the bunnies. The cats each picked a "victim." Sandy and Nonny crouched on the floor like tigers in the jungle. Their eyes grew big, their ears were up straight, their tails lashing behind them. The bunnies, who by now were as big as the cats, pretended not to see them. They played tag around Daddy's foot, leap frog over the table legs and king-of-the-hill from the window seat. Sandy selected Mopsy to pounce on. He caught her just as she dove under the sideboard. She turned quickly, striking out with her powerful hind legs. Sandy was knocked head over tin kettle. He rolled over, sat up, and looked puzzled and offended.

"That should teach Mr. McTavish a lesson," Mummy said.

Mopsy looked at Mom Pom, as if to say, "I hope so."

Daddy asked, "Who would like to go out and chase fireflies?"

"I would, I would," said Wren. "Come on, Mom Pom, come on Marie, come on Shanty. Let's ignore the dinner dishes."

"O. K.," agreed Mom Pom. "Let's go."

"I'll get the jar." Marie raced off.

The evening was sort of purple and soft and sweet. The Killileas caught the beautiful little insects very carefully so they would not be hurt. Daddy ran, carrying Wren, and Mom Pom ran along beside them. Marie went off by herself to see if she could catch more than they did. When the chase was over this night, Marie had won. She had eight and they had five. They put them all in one jar and went up to the girls' room. They sat for a while in the dark, watching the lovely flickering lights of the fireflies.

"Now make your wishes—because it's time for bed," Mom Pom told them. "Then we'll let the fireflies out one by one and each will carry a wish as he leaves to light the dark outside."

(Marie wished, as she always did, that Wren could have crutches and walk.)

"Oh, Mom Pom, not yet, I'm not at all fatigued," Wren begged.

"Sorry," said Mummy—"but right now. It's late."

"Oh, no," Karen persisted.

"Oh, yes," Mummy said firmly.

"I don't want to," Wren whined.

"You must, just the same." Mom Pom started to undo Wren's braces.

"No!" yelled Wren and kicked her foot.

"I'm sorry you did that," said Mummy, "because now I have to slap your leg and you won't be able to go out tomorrow night."

"Oh, Mom Pom, please don't," begged Marie, running over and putting her arm around Karen.

"I must," said Mummy and gave Wren a hard slap on her leg. Wren started to cry. It had really hurt. "It's too bad," Mummy went on, undoing the braces, "but you see when God sends children to a mother and father, he also sends them the job of training these children to obey. When children disobey their parents, they are disobeying God. It hurts me to punish my children—I'd much rather not. But if I didn't, then I would be displeasing God, too."

Wren had stopped crying and was listening intently to what Mummy was saying. So was Marie. They finished undressing in silence. They had their baths and Daddy came in and they all said their night prayers. Mom Pom turned out the light and kissed them good night. She went to the door and stopped there, as she always did. "God bless you," she said.

"Mom Pom," Wren called to her softly.

"Yes, darling?"

"It isn't easy to be a *good* mother—is it?"

"It isn't easy to be a good anything." Mummy came back and sat on the side of Karen's bed. "It wasn't easy to walk up a steep hill alone, carrying a heavy cross—hurt and bleeding and so very tired. But God did it for love of us, so—we do the hard things for love of Him."

"I'm so sorry, Mom Pom." Wren had tears in her eyes. "So sorry I hurt you, but even sorrier I hurt Him."

"I know." Mom Pom kissed her and wiped away her tears. "You've told me. Now, before you go to sleep, tell God you're sorry."

"I will," said Wren. "Good night, Mother dear."

"Good night." And her mother smiled at her very sweetly.

Mummy went to the living room and found Gloria there, talking to Daddy. Daddy said, "Gloria's mother is sick and she has had to go away. I have asked Gloria to come and live with us and be our daughter."

Mom Pom went over to Gloria and kissed her. "I'm sorry that your mother is sick, but you know how much we love you and we will be proud to have you for our daughter."

Gloria threw her arms around Mummy's neck. "Oh, thank you!"

She was crying softly. "I love you, too."

"Dry your eyes," Mummy told her, "and we'll go and tell the children the news."

Wren had just finished telling God she was sorry, when Mom Pom and Gloria came into the room. "I really shouldn't disturb you two," Mummy said laughingly, "but we have such wonderful news I just couldn't keep it 'til morning."

Marie and Wren shouted excitedly, "What news? What is it?" Mummy had her arm around Gloria.

"Do you love Glo?" she teased.

"You know we do," the children told her impatiently. "But what's the news?"

"Well—" said Mom Pom slowly.

"Oh, stop teasing," Marie urged.

"I can't stand the suspense," Wren cried.

Mummy laughed again. "As of tonight, I have *three* children. From now on Glo is going to be your sister and our daughter, just as you are."

The children let out an earsplitting yell. Marie leapt out of bed and threw herself on Gloria, almost knocking her down. Wren held out her arms and Gloria bent over her for her hug. They couldn't see but it sounded almost as though Gloria was crying. "I'm so happy. I'm so happy," she kept saying over and over.

"So am I," said their father from the doorway. "Not many men can brag about *three* daughters as wonderful as mine."

"Ours," corrected Mummy.

"Ours," agreed father. They stood and looked at the three girls. They were as proud as they were happy.

CHAPTER THIRTEEN

NEWS—AND ANOTHER

DADDY grumbled loud and long over night feedings for birds, but he insisted on taking his turns. The little things began to grow rapidly and Mummy put them in the cage with Dunk. He adopted them wholeheartedly and the second day he assumed the task of feeding them. As they grew, a bigger cage was needed for the six birds, so Mom Pom bought an old parrot cage from a junk dealer. She cleaned and polished it and it made a lovely house with plenty of room.

One night Daddy said to his three girls. "I have a surprise for you."

"What is it?" they chorused.

"Have you noticed that Nonny sleeps a lot and has grown very fat?" he asked.

"Yes—"

"Well," said Daddy, "she's going to have kittens."

"When?" Wren demanded.

"Hurray," yelled Marie.

"Maybe they'll have to have night feedings." Glo giggled.

Daddy pretended he didn't hear her.

"I don't know when exactly," he told the girls, "but I should think very soon now."

"I just love baby kittens." Mother was as pleased as the youngsters.

"What fun it will be." Marie hugged herself with glee.

"Nonny won't need any assistance from us," Wren told them seriously. "She will be an excellent mother." Daddy nodded, hiding a smile at the big words.

"I'm sure she will be," he agreed.

As excited as Marie was about the kittens, she still wondered a lot about Wren, and her walking with crutches.

Marie loved Gloria so much, she decided that she would let her share the Game. Gloria was delighted and took great pride in having Marie teach her all the songs and the things you did with them. She said she liked "Gallopy Trot" the best of all.

The Game and the skis and the falling had helped Wren very much. She was now moving her feet one after the other and no one had to push the skis for her any more. She could do it all alone. Her balance was better, too.

One day, Mummy and Daddy took Wren for her regular visit to the cerebral palsy doctor and came home more excited than Marie had ever seen them.

Daddy was calling to Marie and Gloria before he was in the front door. "The most wonderful thing—you'll never guess—the doctor was so pleased—"

"What? What?" They felt they would burst if they had to wait to hear.

Daddy put Karen on a chair and he and Mummy stood beside her. "Wren will tell you," he said and looked as if he would burst, too. So, for that matter, did Mummy.

Wren sat up straight and proud. Her cheeks were pink and her eyes were bright. "I," she said with emphasis, "am ready for *crutches.*"

"You wonderful girl, you!" exclaimed Gloria. "I just can't believe it."

Marie said nothing. She had grown quite pale. Her heart felt tight. She couldn't believe it.

Wren looked at Marie. "She doesn't believe it," she told Mummy and Daddy. "It's true, Honey, it's true." Her voice was squeaky with joy.

Marie ran over and put her head in Wren's lap. "You angel—you blessed, blessed angel!" And her voice was trembly.

"They're being made," Daddy told them, "and should be here in two or three weeks."

Shanty was jumping around as though he understood all that was said.

"We'll go for walks, Shanty," Wren patted him, "just the two of us." He wagged his long, plumed tail so exuberantly that he swept the ash tray and cigarette box off the coffee table and onto the floor. The box broke.

"Who cares?" Mummy was certainly gay. "Nothing could make me unhappy today."

Shanty sat down in front of Karen. She told him, "We'll take a walk the day the crutches come."

Mummy turned to her quickly. "Oh, no, Wren. You mustn't promise him that. He'd be disappointed. The doctor said you will have to practice on them—balance and posture—for some time before you will be able to walk on them."

"How long?" Wren asked.

"A month or two at least," Daddy answered.

"Oh—well, I don't care how long it takes, as long as I'm getting them. Anyway, I'll bet I do it quicker than that."

"I'll bet you do, too," said Glo and Marie together.

The days seemed very long while waiting for the crutches. They all wondered, sometimes, if they would ever come. Mummy called the man who was making them several times. He was very sweet and said he'd finish them as quickly as possible.

Meanwhile, Wren was planning all the things she'd be able to do, once she was walking on crutches. Her family and friends were helping her plan.

Kathy and John suggested, "As soon as you can walk to Vale Place, we'll have a picnic in our back yard. Hot dogs and marshmallows and root beer."

Daddy had one of the happiest thoughts of all. During the summer they had started taking Wren fishing with them. When they went hunting fiddlers for bait, Karen held the can. "Now," said Daddy, "you can CATCH bait, too."

This was a most delightful thought. Fiddlers are little crabs about as big as a quarter. They live in the rich black mud of the banks of Long Island Sound. They build their houses a good distance under the surface of the ground and they have underground tunnels from one house to another. Their doorways are holes in the mud, just a little bigger than the fiddler himself. They make the best bait in the world for blackfish.

"It will be easy," Daddy said. "You can catch them by putting your crutch tip on them and holding them for us until we can pick them up."

"Oh, boy!" Wren exclaimed. "Then I'll be a full-fledged fisherman."

"Full-fledged" Daddy repeated, smiling, "because you'll catch your own bait."

"Wren," Marie said, "what I want to do with you best of all—just the two of us—we'll go off by ourselves in the spring and find the first violets."

Before Karen could say anything, Gloria was planning, "You and I can walk to the corner and you can put Mom Pom's letters in the box."

"It's funny," said Karen, "but sometimes I believe it's true and sometimes I don't."

"Same here," said Marie.

Mummy warned, "But, remember, Sweetheart, its going to take some little while before you'll be able to take any steps on the crutches. You'll have to practice the balancing first."

"I know," Wren agreed, "but maybe not as long as you think."

While they were waiting for the crutches, God sent Karen a present that was so wonderful, so exciting that for weeks the crutches were entirely forgotten. It was a present so tremendous that Wren had never even thought to ask for it.

He sent her a baby! A baby brother!

The day Daddy brought Mom Pom home from the hospital, she walked right up to Karen and put the baby in her arms. Wren couldn't believe this was all *real*. She was sure she must be dreaming and that she'd awake up and find he wasn't there at all.

"He's your baby," said Mummy, "just as you were Marie's. Yours to love and take care of."

Wren looked at her baby. She'd never seen a really little baby before. He was not much bigger than Denise—but all round and pink. He was very beautiful. He had great dark eyes, a nose that tipped up, ears like sea shells and skin that was so soft that Karen said to Mummy, "It doesn't feel like anything." She leaned over and put her face against his cheek. She said to him, "I'm happy but I feel like crying. You're mine—all mine."

Mummy let her hold him a long, long time. He slept and waked and slept again. Wren didn't move. She just sat and looked at him and loved him with her whole heart.

"We've named him Rory," Daddy said. "Do you like it? If not, we'll change it."

"I think it's a lovely name," Wren whispered because she was afraid of waking him. "Rory, Rory, Rory," she said the name over and over. He woke up then, clenched his tiny hands into fists and started to cry.

"What a big cry for such a little baby!" Karen was startled. "Is he hurt, Mom Pom?"

"No, darling, he's just hungry," her mother reassured her. "I'll get his bottle and you can feed him."

"I'll be very gentle," Wren promised.

"Don't worry about that," Daddy said. "He won't break." Mummy went to get the bottle but Gloria got there first.

"Oh, Mom Pom," she said, "it's so wonderful to have a baby! Thank you very much."

Marie was putting the water in the pan for the bottle to be heated. "Mummy," she said, "I know how happy Wren is with her baby because I know how happy I've been with her."

"And I," said Mummy, "am the happiest woman alive—and the luckiest."

Soon the milk was just the right temperature so they went back to Wren and Rory. Daddy was changing the baby's diaper and explaining to Wren just what she should do. After all, if it was her baby, she'd be changing diapers.

Mummy sat Wren way back in the corner of the couch, put Rory in her arms (he was crying as though he were starving) tucked a diaper

under his chin and handed Karen the bottle.

"Marie will tell you just how to do it," said Mummy. "After taking such good care of you, she knows everything about babies."

Rory ate greedily, sucking hard on the nipple. He had one little fist on the bottle. Marie showed Wren how to "bubble" him after every two ounces. She put him on Wren's shoulder and patted his back just the right way. "And remember," she warned, "we always have to support his head—at least until he gets stronger."

When there was still a half ounce in the bottle, Rory fell asleep as quickly as he had waked before. Wren sat and whistled lullabies until it grew dark outside and the street lights blinked on. Then Mummy took Rory, ever so gently, and put him to bed in Karen's room. Wren had a room of her own by now. Marie and Gloria would have liked to have had him sleep with them. But as long as he was Wren's baby, they thought it only right that he sleep with her.

CHAPTER FOURTEEN

THE PACKAGE—AND VICTORY

IN the weeks that followed, Rory grew fast, fat and more gorgeous every day. Wren worked at developing her vocabulary so she might fairly describe him. She said he was "fabulous," "increasingly alert," "captivating," "dextrous," "utterly enchanting."

One morning, Wren was feeding Rory, Daddy was dressing and Mummy was getting breakfast. Daddy came pounding downstairs.

"Of all things," he shouted, "Nonny had her kittens in my bureau drawer—on my shirts!"

Mummy took Rory, and Daddy picked up Wren and they ran up to the bedroom. Sure enough—four kittens. "They look like mice," Karen exclaimed, "so tiny—so sweet! Good girl," she said to Nonny. Nonny was busily washing the kittens but she stopped to look up at them as if to say, "Aren't they lovely? Aren't you proud of me?" She purred at them, telling them how happy she was. Wren stroked her but was careful not to touch the little ones. They squeaked as they nuzzled into their mother's soft fur.

"In a couple of days, their eyes will open," Daddy told the family, "and in about two weeks they will try to walk." He put Karen on a chair where she could sit and watch the kittens and left for work. Marie and Gloria had already gone to school and Wren couldn't wait for them to get home. While she was thinking about how delighted they would be, there was a knock on the front door. Mummy went to open it. Then Wren heard her cry, "They're here! They're here! Your crutches are here, Karen!"

She ran over and put the box on the floor in front of Karen. Her fingers were shaking as she tore off the cord and the paper. Wren sat still, staring at the box as though she were afraid it would vanish. Mummy took off the lid and there were the crutches in all their gleaming beauty.

Wren gasped, "They're beautiful—very beautiful!"

"Aren't they?"

"I want to try them right away," Wren said.

"Right away—this second," Mummy agreed and took them out of the box. She fitted them onto Wren's arms and helped her to stand up. Wren swayed and then steadied herself.

"Now," said Mummy, "just stand for a moment or two and get the feel of them."

Karen stood and then Mummy said, "Let's rest now—and we'll try again."

So Wren rested and stood and rested and stood until Mummy advised, "No more for now, Sweetheart. You'll want to show Daddy and the girls when they come home. If you get too tired, you won't do so well."

There was a whimper from Rory and Mummy put the crutches beside Wren on the chair and went to see if her son was all right. He had become tangled up in his covers so she straightened him out and started back to the bedroom. When she got to the door she looked over to Wren and Wren wasn't in the chair. She had the crutches on and was WALKING!

Mummy stood—unable to move. Wren took a step and another—and another—Mummy was silently counting them. Three, four, five—six, seven, eight—Mummy was holding her breath, nine, ten—Karen's face was drawn with strain and chalky white. There was perspiration on her forehead and upper lip. Eleven, twelve, thirteen, fourteen—Wren swayed and then steadied. *Fifteen, sixteen*—Mummy could stay still no longer. She rushed across the room and took Wren and her crutches into her arms. Mummy cried and cried—she couldn't stop.

"Did you see me? Did you see me?" Wren was shrieking in her excitement. "I can walk—I can walk—*I can walk all by myself!*"

Mummy tried to stop crying. She couldn't, she was too happy.

Wren said, "You only cry when you're happy—I'm so glad."

Marie could hardly wait for school to be out the next day. She hurried home, tossed her book bag on the kitchen table and ran out. She went from house to house, to all her friends, telling them, "Be at our house at three-thirty this afternoon. We have a big surprise for you. Don't bring your dog today." And she dashed away.

Gloria and Marie had planned carefully. At three-thirty, Wren was sitting on a chair, trying to look calm, but her eyes were glittering with excitement. The crutches were leaning beside her, covered with a doll's blanket. When fourteen children were assembled, Marie stood in the center of the room. They stopped their chatter and looked at her expectantly. She said, "Karen has something to show you and you couldn't guess what it is." Marie pointed to the blanket. The children leaned forward, watching the blanket. "All right, Wren," said Marie, and Karen seized the blanket and pulled it off the crutches.

The children gasped and there was a long *"Oh-oh-oh-oo-oo!"* They raced across the room to Wren. "They're pretty!" "Look at them shine!" "Real leather!" They were all talking at once. "May I try them?" May I?" "MAY I?"

"Take it easy," Mummy called above the noise. "You can all have a turn, but we have another surprise first." Karen clapped her hand to her mouth to keep from telling instead of *doing*. "Are you ready, Wren?"

"Yes—" she whispered.

Marie handed Karen the crutches and the children stood silent and amazed as Karen put them on. She placed the crutch tips about a foot ahead of her, she bent over, she straightened up—*she took a step—*

A great *"Oh-oh-o-o-"* started from the children and swelled into a jubilant shout as Wren took another step—and another. Marie and Gloria walked beside her—their heads high with pride. Then her friends rushed at Karen. Marie grabbed her to keep her from being knocked down. Glo took the crutches. Mummy stole quietly from the room and left Wren to her great victory.

From that day on, Mummy left many chores undone. She and Wren practiced early and late. This was the best of the whole Game. "Just imagine," said Mummy to everyone she spoke to, "the doctor thought it would take several months of practice before Wren could take a step!" Daddy, of course, was saying the same thing to everyone he met. So were Gloria and Marie. They were all so proud of their Wren.

Wren had to learn that when you move your right foot you swing your left arm, and when you move your left foot you swing your right arm. To help her remember this, Mummy tied a pink ribbon on the right crutch and left shoe, and a blue ribbon on the left crutch

and the right shoe, so she would move the same color at the same time.

While Wren was learning to walk, Rory was learning to crawl and then toddle. He had trouble with both. He was so fat. He'd just get going when he'd topple over. He'd get so mad he'd sit and yell and yell. When no one paid any attention to his yelling, he'd stop, get up, laugh and start toddling all over again.

He started talking younger than most children, Daddy said because he was with Wren so much and she chattered all the time. The first word Rory said was "Kawan." Karen was immensely pleased by this.

When Mummy and Karen were playing the Game on the crutches, Rory would toddle along beside her, calling, "Boo cwotch, boo foot, ping cwotch, ping foot," helping her to remember, to be sure, but sometimes making her laugh so hard she'd have to stop walking. Her balance wasn't good but his was worse. "He falls much more than I do," Karen would say as he tumbled beside her.

And Rory was generous in his praise. Every other step Wren took he would chant, "Good Kawan, wulling (walking)."

There was, however, one member of the family who didn't like the crutches. That was Shanty. He didn't trust them. He wanted his little girl on something solid, trusting to something that moved. When Karen put the crutches on, he'd lay directly in front of her so she couldn't move them. He'd put his head down between his paws and whimper. She'd push the crutch tip against his side and plead with him to "Get out of the way." He'd refuse. Then she'd get angry and scold. He wouldn't even raise his head. Mummy and Daddy and Gloria and Marie would scold. He'd pay no attention whatsoever. So for months and months, every time Wren got on her crutches, her four-footed guardian angel had to be dragged away. He had to be locked in another room where he would sit and howl wildly until the Game was over.

There were no idle moments in Wren's days. The exercise part of the Game was continued, the crutch walking, and she was busy with her friends but most specially with Rory. He could be a problem. He got into all sorts of mischief, but was so sweet she couldn't scold. He learned to climb out of his crib and every morning Mummy would find him curled up in bed with Karen.

At long last Shanty accepted the crutches. Then he and Karen took walks together. They went visiting. Karen caught bait, just as Daddy had promised she would. She went on picnics in Vale Place. The kittens played tag in and out and around her crutches and the bunnies nibbled the rubber tips.

"I have moths in my crutches," Wren told Mom Pom, remembering the rug and piano.

"I'll call the exterminator," Mom Pom replied.

"I think you ought to make a stew of those troublesome bunnies," Daddy teased. And then the children would all yell, "Oh, you cruel, cruel man! How would you like to be put into a stew?"

Rory always yelled along with the others, though he didn't understand the joke at all.

"What a delectable stew our brother would make," Karen would say. "There's so much fat on him."

"Good tew, good tew," Rory would agree and clap his hands.

CHAPTER FIFTEEN

CHRISTMAS

IT was a week before Christmas. It was the night of the Search.

The Search was a family adventure that came once a year. It was the Search for the biggest and most beautiful Christmas tree that could be found.

The Search was always conducted at night. All the family went. They loved the bright Christmas lights hung along the streets and the gay decorations in the brightly lit shops. Best of all they liked to Search in the snow—and this night it was snowing. There was great excitement. They had to dress warmly, for it was very cold. At last they were ready to set out. Everyone was bundled up with snowsuits, scarves, caps and mittens. Rory had so many clothes on he could just barely put one little foot in front of the other. With his bright cheeks and starry eyes he looked like one of Santa's Helpers in his red suit

with its peaked hat.

Everyone piled into the car, including Shanty, and they started off. They sang Christmas Carols as they drove. *Holy Night, Oh Little Town of Bethlehem, It Came Upon a Midnight Clear, Adeste Fidelis* and many others.

Each time they came to a place that sold trees they all got out to look at them. After all, it was the family's tree and every member of the family had to approve it. Not finding one grand enough, they would all pile back into the car and start off again.

It got colder and colder and the snow fell heavier and heavier, wrapping all the world in white stillness. Wren put part of her blanket over Shanty. He couldn't sing to keep warm.

After several unsuccessful stops they began to wonder if they would ever find *It*. Daddy said, "I wonder if we should give up?"

The children chorused, "No!" Wren added, "We are determined and courageous."

"In that case," said Daddy, "we should have something to keep our courage up. Let's get some hot chocolate and buns."

"Hurray!"

"Wonderful!"

"I'm famished," Wren told them.

"Wawy famist," said her brother.

Daddy took them to a little shop that was panelled in pine wood that gleamed in the lamp light and there were holly boughs and chains of greens around the walls. In the center of each table there was a red candle burning brightly. Rory tried to blow it out. The chocolate was hot and sweet and it warmed them all over. They were singing more loudly than ever when they started off again.

They turned up a little side street and there beside a tiny white house they saw It. Mummy called out, "Stop the car—there it is! I can tell from here."

Daddy pulled into the driveway and they all got out. Shanty danced around in the snow as they went over to make sure that this tree was surely It. Rory wasn't interested in the tree but he looked at the white snow covering everything and said, "Muk–Kawan see muk." Muk in Rory's language was "milk" and so far as he was concerned, the world was covered with milk.

Daddy held the tree upright so they could walk around it and judge. It was more than twice as tall as he was. Its branches were so thick they couldn't see the trunk. It was a dark blue green and the lower branches swept the earth. It was so wide that four of them couldn't link arms around it.

"I think it has been waiting for us, Daddy," Marie said.

"It looks glad we've come," Gloria agreed.

"I know it wants us to take it," Wren told them.

"Gimme," said Rory, holding out his plump little hands.

"This is the loveliest tree ever," said Mummy softly, caressing a bough.

"That settles it," Daddy decided.

On the way home they sang *Oh Christmas Tree*–that is, all but Rory. He fell asleep in Karen's lap. They talked about the beautiful ornaments in the boxes in the attic. Their tree would be dressed as royalty.

As soon as they reached home, Mom Pom and Daddy bundled the children into bed. They were so tired they fell asleep almost instantly. Karen dreamt that the tree put its arms around her and its topmost branch kissed her lightly on the forehead and the tree whispered, "Thank you for choosing me."

The next day the whole family joined in setting up the crèche. They made the hills and valleys covered with snow. They put the pine branches around the stable and the forest on the hill. They stood

Mary and Joseph beside the manger and the cow and the donkey at the foot of the manger. The Shepherd Boy and his daddy were off in the field, hurrying toward the stable. They put the flock on the side of the hill to graze, with the dogs guarding the sheep. The bunnies were hopping across the snow and the squirrel and the mouse were in their corner of the stable. And the goats were on the path. The manger was filled with straw and then, most lovingly, they placed the Baby with His arms outstretched toward them.

Daddy suspended a lovely star over the stable and there were invisible wires holding angels as they hovered over their new-born King.

Mom Pom had bought four new little lambs. One for each of her children. They all said their night prayers in front of the stable and when they were finished Mummy said, "Here is a lamb for each of you. I am going to put them in the field."

"Pwetty," said Rory.

Mummy continued, "Each night, when we have finished our prayers, this is what we shall do. If you have been good children, you may move your lamb along the path to the stable. If you've been naughty, the lamb must stay where he is until the next night. If you're very, very good, you should all get your lambs to the manger by Christmas Eve. I think the Baby Jesus would think that the best birthday present —to have you all so good that there would be four lambs waiting for Him at His crib the night He is born."

Marie was thinking of the night she had knelt before the Baby and asked Him, "Dear Baby Jesus, Christmas is Your birthday. Couldn't *You* bring Karen a present? Please, please help Mummy and Daddy find a doctor who will teach Karen to use her arms and legs. Please, Baby. Thank You." She thought how good the Baby Jesus had been to her—to them all. She thought most people didn't ask Him enough. She thought how much He had done for Wren. How could she ever thank Him. After the others had left, she knelt alone in front of the manger and told Him. "Thank you, Baby Jesus. Thank you very much." Was it the flickering of the candles or did the Baby smile?

The days before Christmas are always the longest days of the year. This year they seemed longer than ever. Daddy put up two cots in Wren's room for Gloria and Marie, because the children always slept together Christmas Eve.

They were all very happy and a little proud when this Holy Night came because the four little lambs were close against the manger.

In this house, there was a custom which was dear to all the family. On Christmas morning, before they went to the tree and the presents for the material part of Christmas, they went to greet the Baby.

It was still dark when they awoke. The snow lay like a blessing on all the world. Marie and Gloria put on their robes and helped Wren and Rory on with theirs. Rory chanted "Huwwy, huwwy—wanna see the Baby." They put the crutches on Wren and went to wake Mom Pom and Daddy.

All together, but softly, they started up to the crib, singing *Silent Night, Holy Night.* The candles were burning steadily and the star hung bright over the stable.

"All is calm, all is bright—"

With hearts overflowing with love of the Baby, they reached the manger and finished their song.

As they stood there, Wren moved close and then—she did a marvelous thing!

She took off one crutch and balanced without help on the other. She stretched out her hand and placed it ever so tenderly on the foot of

BOB RIGER

the Baby. And using only *one* crutch, standing proud and tall, she sang in her high, sweet voice:

"Happy Birthday to You
Happy Birthday to You

The others joined their glad voices with hers,

"Happy Birthday, Baby Jesus,
Happy Birthday to you."

MARIE KILLILEA

was born in New York City, educated in a convent, and graduated into The Depression. This, in itself, blasted her life's ambition to be a doctor. Instead, she took a secretarial course, and—jobs being scarce in 1932—sought substitute work. In the first two and a half years, she worked for twenty-three concerns. This experience was valuable later, when circumstances thrust her into administrative and legislative work.

Marie Killilea's first book, KAREN, was a best-seller three weeks after publication, and received a number of awards. Nationally known as a lecturer, she limits her speaking engagements as well as her writing (she is working on a sequel to KAREN at the present time) to meet the demands of a growing family, as well as to handling the volume of correspondence since the publication of KAREN. So far, there have been over 12,000 letters, and "Courtesy requires that each letter be answered personally," she says. "It's a big job, but a most happy one."

She lives with her husband, four children and their menagerie, in Larchmont, New York. Theirs is an old, three-story Victorian house which the Killileas describe as "grotesquely beautiful." It overlooks Long Island Sound, which Marie Killilea says is a delight but also a snare, since the temptation to watch water and gulls, rather than a manuscript, is almost irresistible.

BOB RIGER

is a New Yorker and a Pratt Institute graduate. After serving as an officer in the United States Merchant Marine and Navy during World War II, he divided six years of staff work between a national magazine and art directing in an ad agency. Now a free lance magazine artist, WREN is his first venture in full length book illustration.

Bob Riger and his wife, Eleanor, live in a big house in Brooklyn, New York, with their two children, Christopher Robin and Victoria Eleanor.